For Debbie, Daniel, and Michael

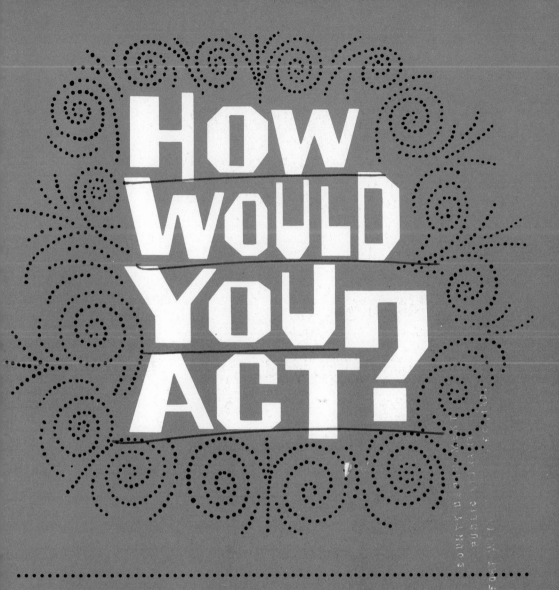

HOW WOULD YOU ACT?

By Ruth and Stan Brod

Rand McNally & Company

CHICAGO   NEW YORK   SAN FRANCISCO

How would
you act
if you were a cat?

I'd eat mice
and grow fat.

↑

UP

How would you act
if you were a fox?

I'd run from the hounds
and hide in a box.

How would
you act if you were
a snail?

I'd glide through
the garden, leaving
a trail.

How would you act if you were an owl?
I'd hoot and I'd howl.

How would you act if you were a whale?

I'd sail in a pail.

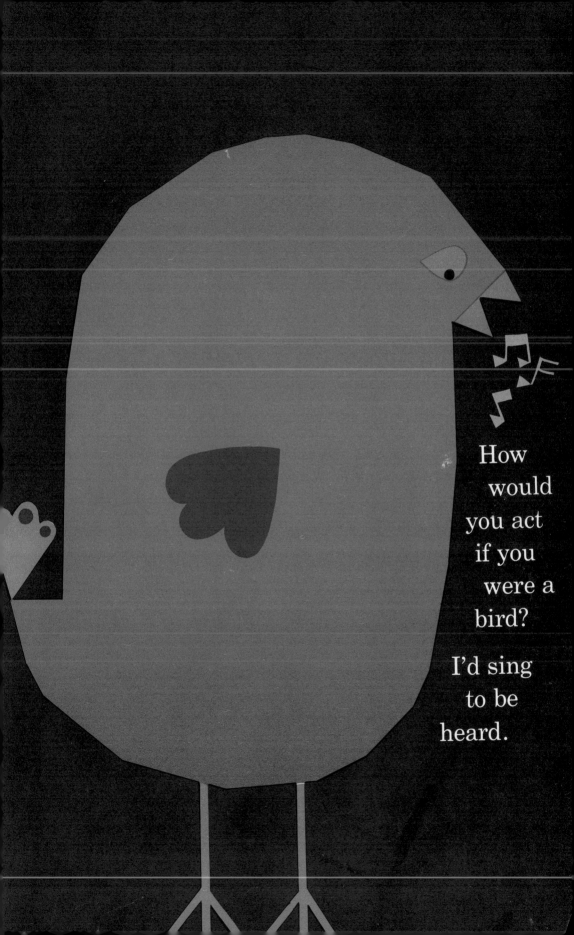

How
would
you act
if you
were a
bird?

I'd sing
to be
heard.

How would you act
if you were a frog?

I'd croak on a log.

How would you act if you were a cricket?

I'd jump from thicket to thicket to thicket.

How would you act
if you were a kangaroo?

I'd play peek-a-boo.

How would you act if you were a seal?

I'd juggle a ball and balance a wheel.

How would you act
if you were a raccoon?
I'd live on the moon.

How would you act
   if you were a sheep?

I'd graze in the grass
   and then fall asleep.

How would
you act if you
were a giraffe?

I'd eat leaves
from the trees
and make all
of you laugh.

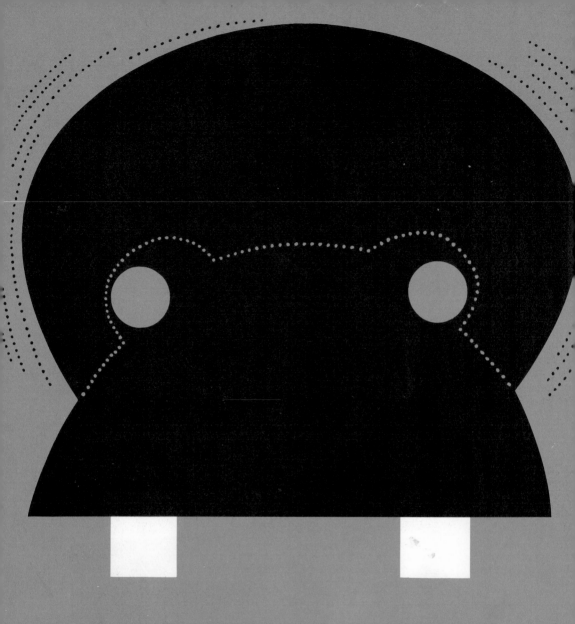

How would you act

if you were a hippo?

I'd take a dip-o.

How would you act

if you were a goat?

I'd eat up your coat.

How would you act if you were a yak?

I'd carry a pack on my hairy back.

How would you act if you were a butterfly?

I'd flit and I'd flutter up in the sky.

How would you act
if you were a mole?

I'd wait until dark
to come out of my hole.

How would you act if you were a porcupine?
I'd stiffen my spines, and dine on a vine.

How would you act if you were a worm?
I'd live in the earth and squirm.

How would you act

if you were a fish?

I'd swish in a dish.

How would you act if you were just you?